My BIG Book of MONSTER Fun

PaRragon

Bath · New York · Cologne · Melbourne · Delhi
Hong Kong · Shenzhen · Singapore · Amsterdam

This edition published by Parragon Books Ltd in 2015

Parragon Books Ltd
Chartist House
15–17 Trim Street
Bath BA1 1HA, UK
www.parragon.com

ISBN 978-1-4723-9202-2

Printed in China

My Big Book of Monster Fun

Contents

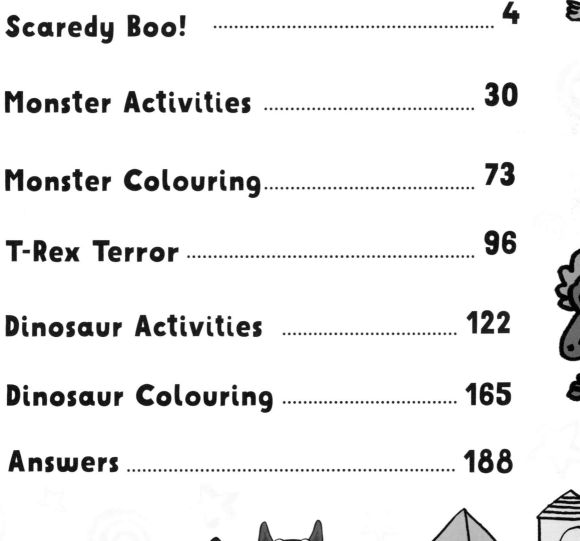

Scaredy
BOO!

Under the bed lived a monster,
A monster named **Scaredy Boo.**
Boo was afraid of everything.
He would have been scared of you!

Each night, the other small monsters
Raced round the house having fun.
Though all the children were sleeping,
Boo feared they'd WAKE UP someone!

Boo sighed, "I'm frightened of **Big** Things.
Small Things and Wiggly Things too!
I'm little Scaredy Boo monster.
Wouldn't these things scare YOU?"

Scaredy Boo didn't like noises,
Things that went crackle or *squeak*.
Hearing strange whispers and rustles
Made poor Boo's legs go all **weak!**

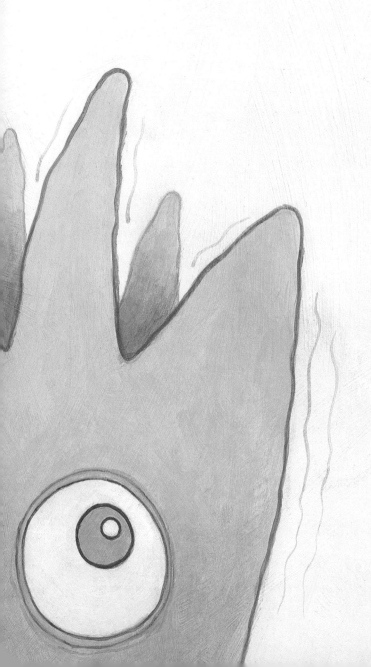

Boo was afraid of things *Tickly*,
Things that had Big Furry Ears,
Things that had noses all Twitchy –
These were Boo's worst monster fears!

Late one night, Boo heard **loud** footsteps.
"**Help!** Something's out there!" he said.
"Hello," the Thing called. "You hiding?"
It peeked at Boo under the bed.

Scaredy Boo trembled, "Who are you?
I jump when someone shouts BOO!
I'm little Scaredy Boo monster.
Wouldn't YOU be scared too?"

"Why are you scared?" smiled the stranger.
"I'm Spike – a monster like you!
Come out, and let's **play** together.
Playing's what monsters do!"

Poor Boo felt ever so worried.
He'd never been out before.
Night-time was all **dark** and **scary!**
Creakity-creak, creaked the floor.

"Come on!" Spike called to Boo kindly.
"Let's play with all of these toys!"
"Shh!" Scaredy whispered. "THE CHILDREN!
You'll wake them with all of the noise!"

Boo saw a huge **BLACK SHAPE** looming!
Oh, what a horrible sight!
"**Help!**" he cried, diving for cover.
There he sat, shaking with fright.

Scaredy Boo stuttered, "Wh-hat is that?
I jump when someone shouts **BOO!**
I'm little Scaredy Boo monster.
Wouldn't **YOU** be scared too?"

"That's just your shadow!" Spike told Boo.
"Everything has one - look, see?"
Scaredy Boo felt a little bit silly:
"All I was scared of was ME!"

Just then Boo stopped with a quiver.
"Wh-what's that?" he pointed with fear.
"Big-eared and floppy and furry!
It's much too scary around here!"

"That's just a teddy bear!" Spike said.
Boo asked him, "Do teddies bite?"
"No!" Spike laughed. "Teddies are **friendly!**
They love to cuddle at night!"

"**Help!** There's a Twitchy Thing!" Boo gasped.
Spike grinned, "It's only a **MOUSE!**"
"Oooh! It's quite friendly!" Boo giggled.
"I like exploring this house!"

Scaredy Boo met **ALL** of the monsters.
"It's so much fun playing," he said.
"Thank you, Spike – I'm glad you found me.
It's lonely under the bed!"

WHEEE! From a shelf dropped a spider.
Scaredy Boo's fur stood on end!
"I still don't like spiders!" Boo giggled.
"They scare me too!" laughed his friend.

Boo shouted, "Let's play tomorrow!
It's so *exciting* and *new*!"
"Shh!" all his monster friends whispered.
"YOU'RE NOISY NOW, LITTLE BOO!"

Monster Activities

Complete these monster activities, then turn to page 188 to find the answers.

Which monster shape comes next in each row? Draw its picture.

What has this goblin's mummy given him for lunch?
Draw some revolting food in his lunch box.

It's lunchtime at Goblin School.
Draw what's on the menu today.

Finish drawing these monster pets.

34

Make these trolls identical twins.

Draw pointy teeth, spots and a runny nose on this troll, so that he looks exactly like his twin.

All sorts of things get stuck in this giant's beard. Draw bones, birds' nests and spiders in it.

This greedy monster has been eating lots of food. Draw some more food in his belly!

Give these monster mouths the right number of teeth.

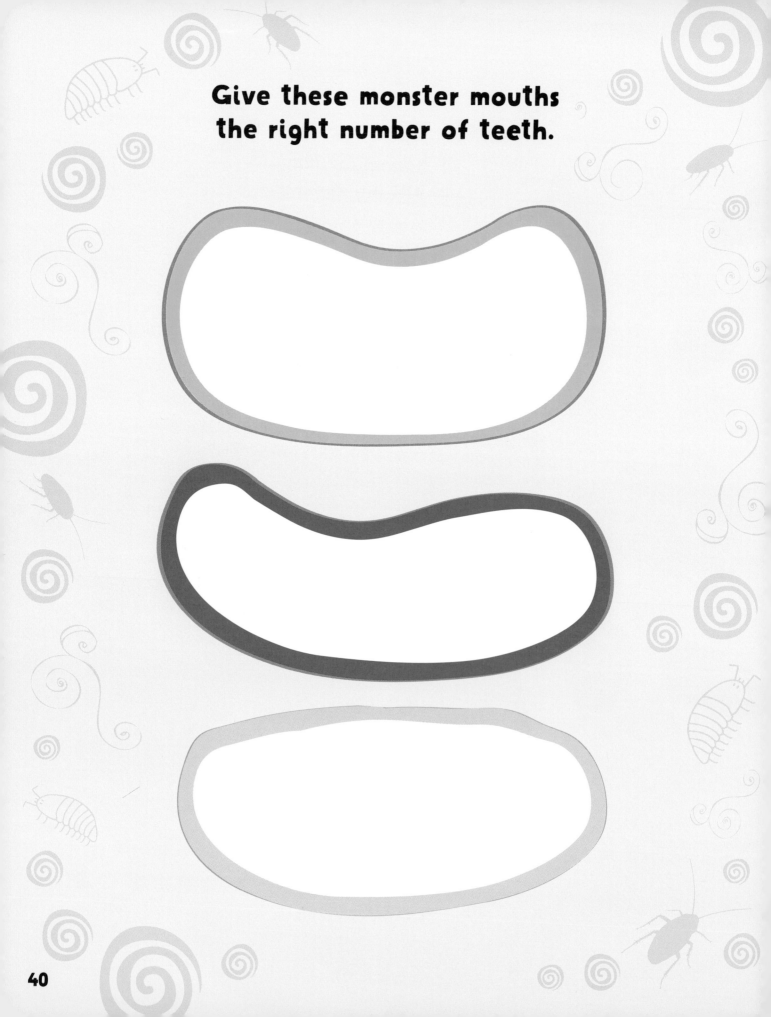

Yuck! Colour this alien's tongue in gross colours.

Draw and colour the items in the jars and bottles on this sweet shelf.

Purple Bon Bons

Yellow Fizz

Pink Pips

Crunchy Capsules

Sweet Surprises

Gloop

Honey Melt

Jelly Mounds

Fruity Fluff

Bubble Burst

Can you find five monsters in the ball pool? Tick the boxes as you find them.

Draw a big ball for this monster to throw.

MONSTER BITE

When monsters aren't busy eating dirty socks and scaring people, they love to have fun, just like you!

He's completely batty!

How many bats are there?
Colour the number.

789

Get ready – the slime race is on!
Follow the tangled lines to find out who wins.

Aargh! Who's that in the mirror?
Draw and colour in the reflection.

Eeek! Can you escape the bog monster? Find and circle five differences in the bottom picture.

Tick your favourite monsters.

51

Which monster shape comes next in each row?
Draw its picture.

Which one of these trails leads to the slug monster?

1

2

3

Can you spot four differences in the bottom picture?

Help the baby monsters get across the swamp to their mummy on the other side!

These scientists are inventing a
new animal – the mucky slime monster!

Draw the missing body
parts to finish it off.

Which shadow matches the fire-breathing dragon?

Put the monsters in order.

Which monster is the smallest?	Which monster has the most eyes?	Which monster has the most feet?

Draw in the missing footprints to connect each monster to its trail.

MONSTER BITE

If you ever see great big footprints in the mud, whatever you do, don't follow them - they might have been made by a monster!

How many little
slime monsters
can you count?

This zombie doesn't have a brain. Which line of footprints leads him to one?

Circle the shadow that matches this zombie exactly.

63

Finish drawing these zombies in the graveyard, then colour them in.

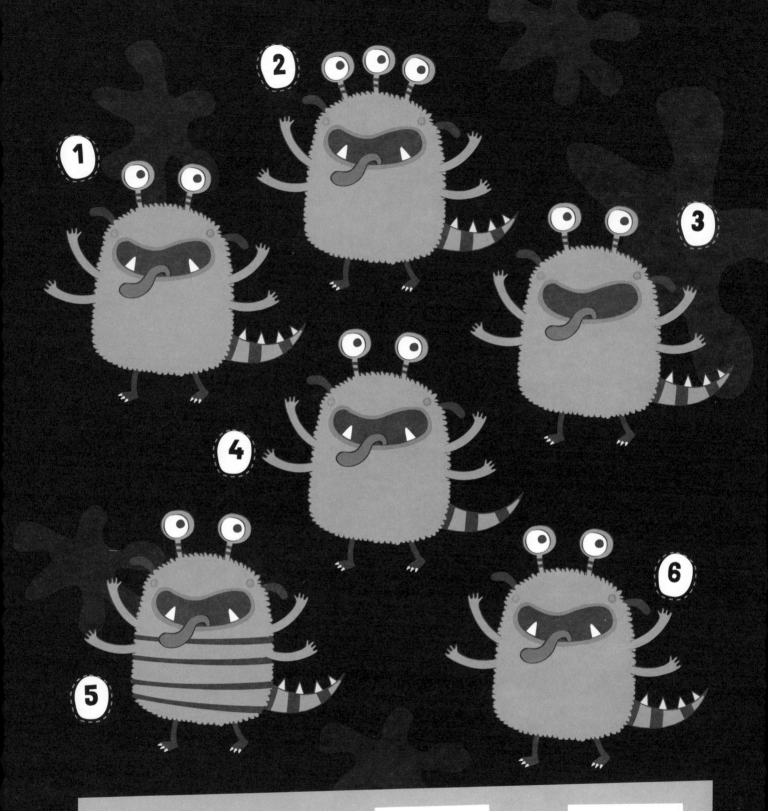

Which two monsters look exactly the same?   and

Give these monsters some brothers and sisters!

Draw another monster that's bigger than these two.

Draw another monster that's smaller than these two.

Draw another monster the same size as these two.

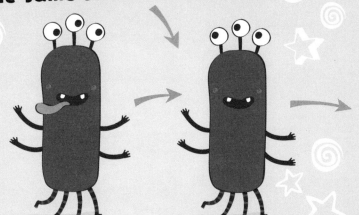

What is each monster eating?
Follow the squiggly lines to find out.

I'm starving!

1

2

3

MONSTER BITE

Monsters are always hungry. They would eat all day and all night long if they could!

1 ----------
2 ----------
3 ----------

How many legs does each sausage monster have? Write it in the circles.

Draw your own sausage monster in this space.

70

How many mummy monsters can you count?

Who has the most eyes?

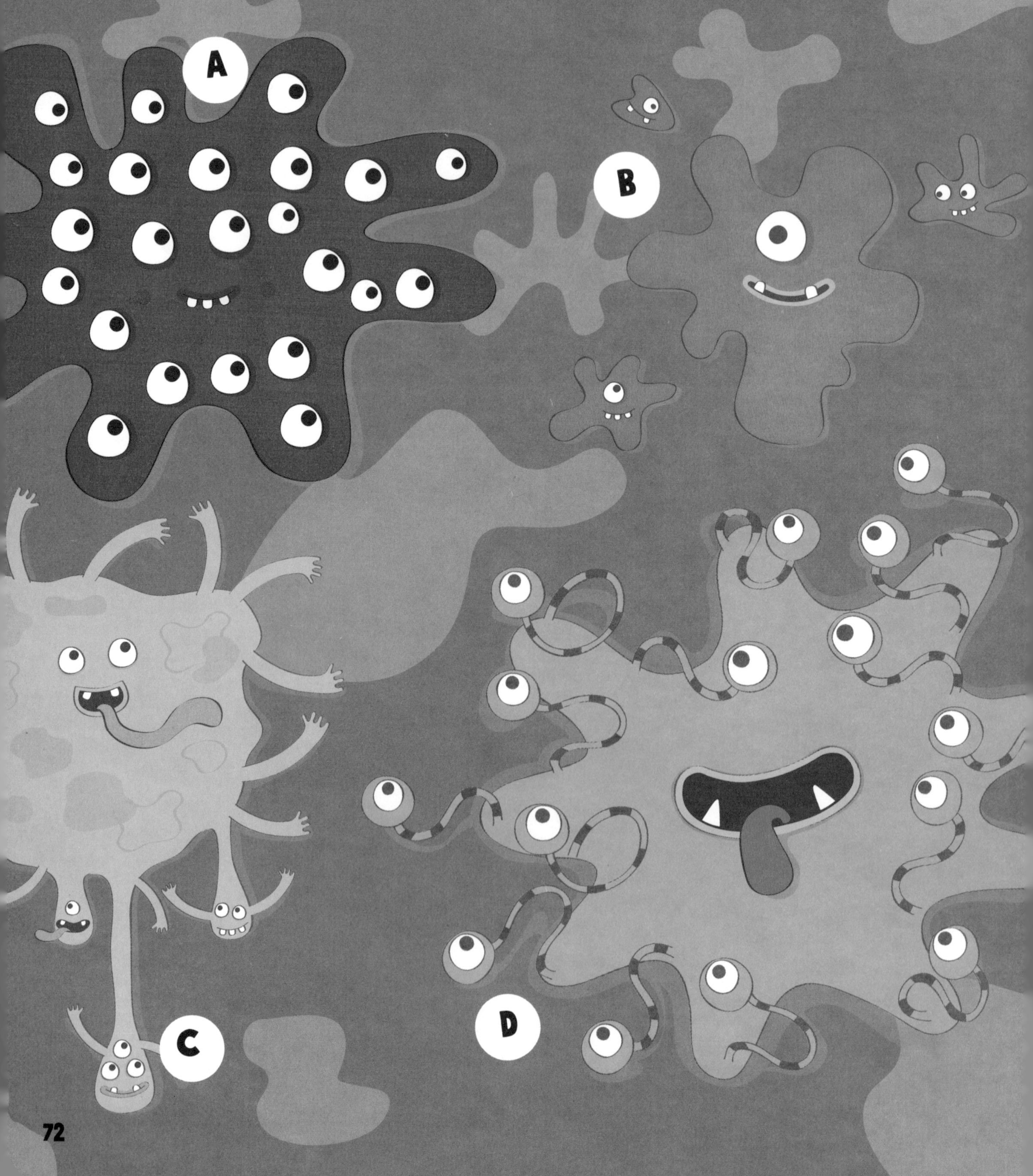

A

B

C

D

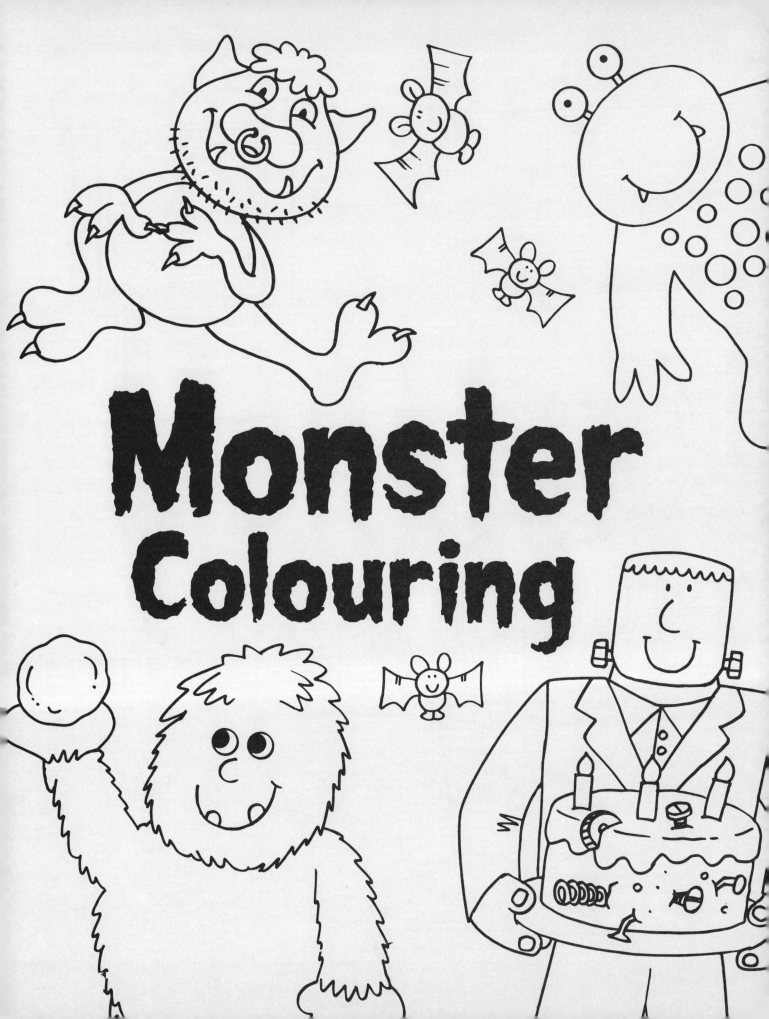

Monster
Colouring

T-REX TERROR

THE SUPERSAURUS LEGEND BEGINS...

65 million years ago...

A radioactive meteorite hurtles through outer space, heading straight for planet Earth...

And the bustling dinotropolis of New Dino City!

IS IT A PTERODACTYL?

IS IT A PLANE?

ARE WE GOING TO BECOME EXTINCT?

Meanwhile, in Cretaceous Park, four young dinos are playing dinoball, but their lives are about to CHANGE FOR EVER!

As the dust settles, Terra begins to cough.

The four friends walk home, full of questions...

Suddenly, from a nearby bank, they hear a cry for...

It's another Raptor robbery! But if those pesky predators think they'll get away THIS time, they're in for a SUPER surprise...

And in that electrifying moment, the LEGEND begins!

In no time, the SUPERSAURS are the talk of New Dino City...

ANOTHER CRIME FOILED!
Criminals car-n't believe it!

SUPERSAURS COLLECT ONE MILLION DINODOLLAR REWARD!
Crime does pay – if your job is to stop it!

PAY: DINO SUPERSAURS
ONE MILLION DINODOLLARS
1,000,000

The Daily Reptile · NEW DINO CITY

MAYOR OPENS HI-TECH SUPERSAURUS HQ!

"Honest Al" Allosaur, Mayor of NDC, says "City safe with the Supersaurs!"

NEW DINO CITY SWOOPERS SIGN DOC!
New signing to STRETCH Swooper winning streak.

Before long, the Supersaurs have rid New Dino City of crime and things are all quiet at Supersaurus HQ.

Doc loves his gadgets, but there's something not quite right about this giveaway...

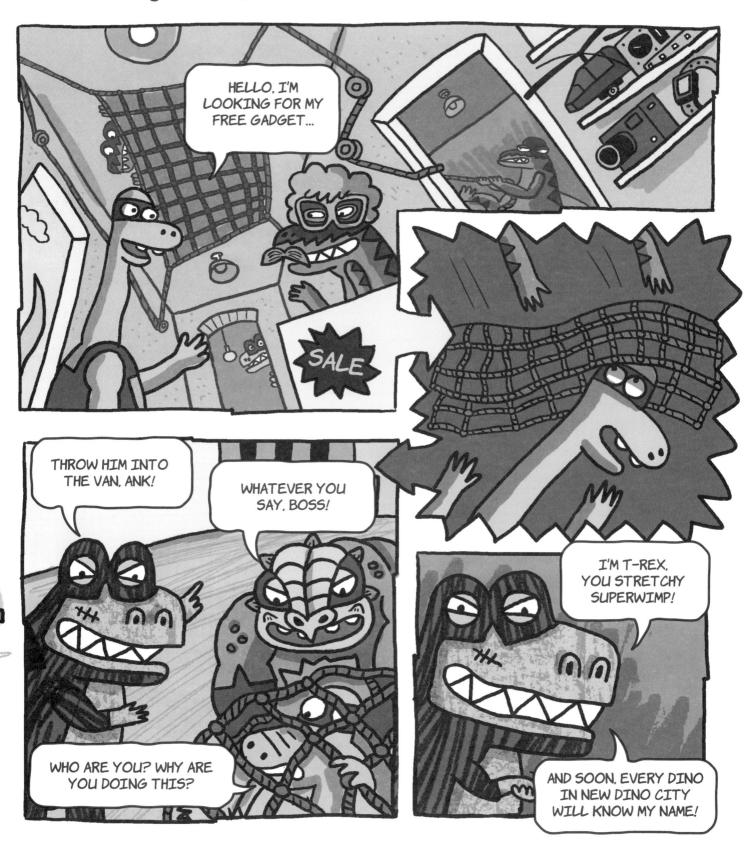

Back at Supersaurus HQ, Trix is monitoring the bay around New Dino City. He's picked up some movement on Volcano Island.

When suddenly every monitor is tuned to...

The Supersaurs spring into action!

109

Oh, no! Is this the end for the Supersaurs?

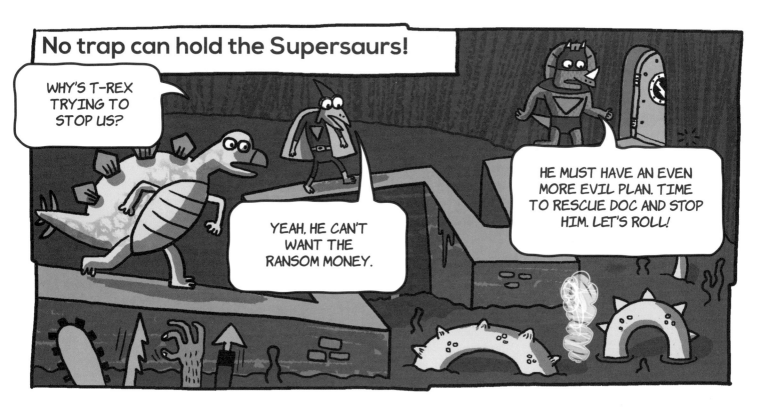

No trap can hold the Supersaurs!

But T-Rex isn't beaten yet!

117

With the team at full strength, the Sinistaurs don't stand a chance!

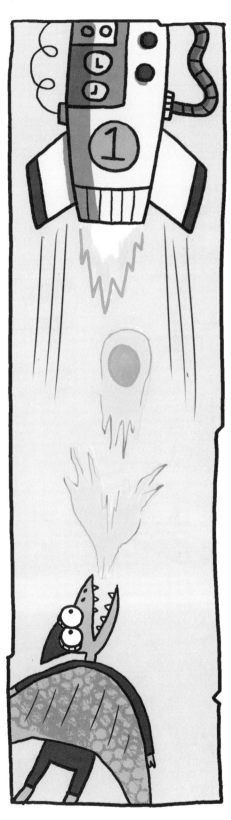

Can Terra stop the rocket in time?

With only seconds to spare, Terra's fireball smashes the rocket out of the sky!

And so the city is safe... until next time!

DINOSAUR ACTIVITIES

Complete these dinosaur activities, then turn to page 190 to find the answers.

Trix is leader of the Supersaurs!
Help him fill his missing pieces.

Write the number next to each jigsaw piece
to show where it belongs in the picture of Trix.

a ☐   b ☐   c ☐   d ☐

Now design an awesome frame for your picture.

Your mission: Find all these names in the wordsearch on the other page!

SUPERSAUR

TERRA

TRIx

STEG

DOC

RAPTORS

T-REx

D	O	C	H	A	G	C	S	X
M	A	Q	R	H	R	G	U	T
P	R	L	G	N	A	B	P	Z
C	R	T	U	U	P	D	E	D
S	E	R	H	T	T	V	R	B
T	T	E	Z	R	O	Y	S	I
E	Z	X	T	I	R	V	A	T
G	K	N	A	X	S	V	U	P
O	J	O	N	R	E	N	R	V

There's one more word to find. Ank is the name of this evil dino! Can you find it in the grid?

127

All dinos love ice cream sundaes! Give these some colour!

ICE CREAM PARLOUR

These dinosaurs won't stop talking.
Fill the speech bubbles with dino chatter!

Steg has powered down. Help him find a route through the park to avoid the Sinistaurs.

Start

Follow the lines to match the Supersaurs and Sinistaurs to their catchphrases!

Poor Mr Mayor doesn't have a catchphrase.
Can you think of one for him?

Volcano Island is a dangerous place! Look closely and circle eight differences in the bottom picture.

The citizens of New Dino City are talking about where T-Rex could be hiding his giant airship...

- ☐ Spot the dino wearing the yellow hat.
- ☐ Find the dino who is stealing food.
- ☐ Can you see two pink dinos?

WANTED

Complete the 'wanted' poster by doodling T-Rex's airship.

T-REX AND HIS GIANT AIRSHIP
REWARD 100,000 DINODOLLARS

Learn to draw Steg. Use the grid on the opposite page to copy the picture, square by square!

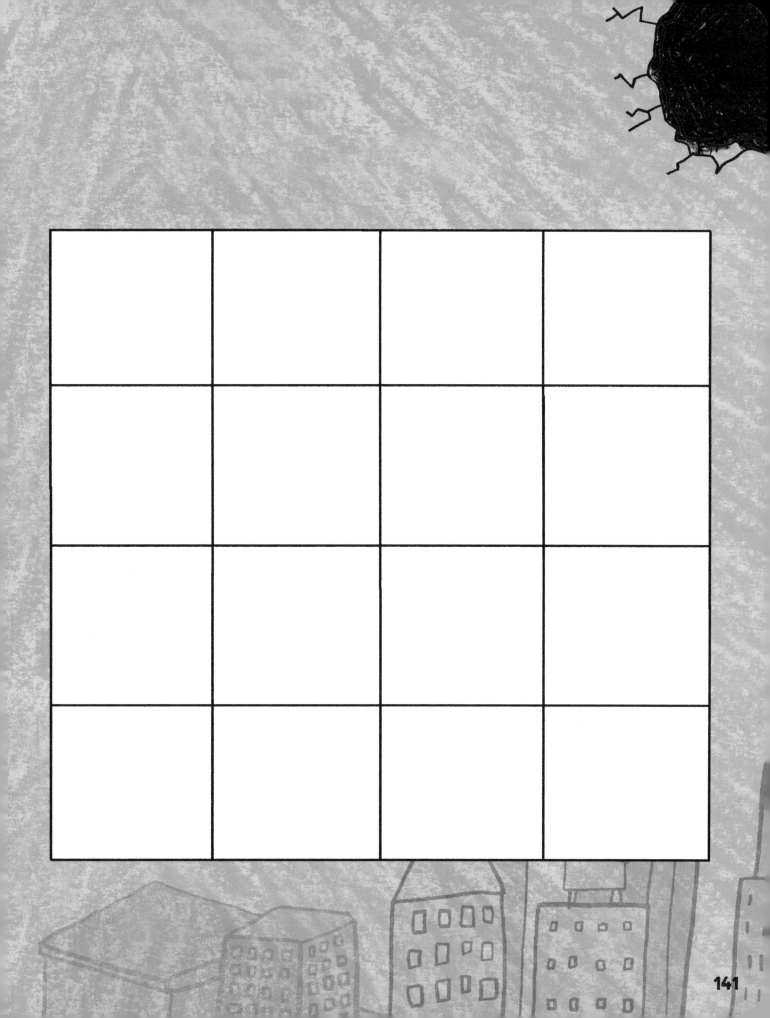

Doc's running late! Play the game to help him catch up with the other Supersaurs. Use a game piece and a dice to move around the board from start to finish.

You will need:
A game piece
A dice

20	GREAT STRETCHING! MOVE FORWARD 5 SPACES.	22	23
19			
WHOA, IT'S A TRAP! MOVE BACK TO SQUARE 7			
17	16	15	14
Start	1	2	3	4

27

Finish

24 | 25 | 26

13 | VERY SPEEDY! MOVE FORWARD 3 SPACES. | 11 | OH NO, RAPTOR ATTACK! MISS A GO!

9

5 | 6 | 7 | 8

The New Dino City underground is mega busy!

Can you spot all of these things?

Terra swoops and soars over New Dino City. Colour her in!

MAKE ROOM FOR MY ZOOM!

What's she saying? Use a mirror to work out her message.

....

T-Rex Is On The Rampage! wAtch Out, Dinos...

Use the coloured dots to complete the picture as fast as you can!

GO TRIX!

LET'S ROLL!

Trix is after T-Rex. Help him pick the right route through the city.

A B C

150

Steg is so strong, even when he's not Super Steg he can lift a car! Colour him and his workshop.

How many spanners does Steg have in his workshop?

1. What has T-Rex stolen?

----

2. Why does T-Rex need the meteorite?
To power a turbo car ☐
To power a cosmic laser ☐
3. Is it hot or cold at the volcano?

----

4. Where do the Supersaurs return the cup to?
New Dino City Bank ☐   Swooper Stadium ☐

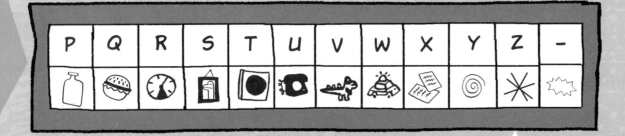

The Supersaurs are always ready to save the day. Crack the code to reveal these HELP messages.

H E L P !   T - R E X

_____ !   _____

I S   A T T A C K I N G !

_____   _____ !

These dino names have been scrambled. Work out who they are!

XRIT ....

COD ....

GETS ....

Crack the code to get into T-Rex's hideout! Colour what comes next in each row?

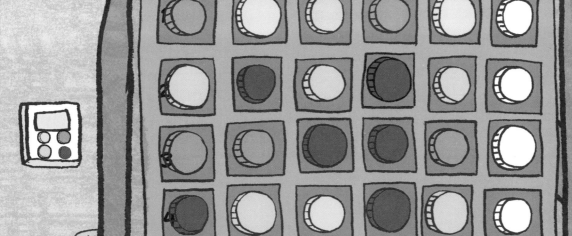

The Supersaurs are setting sail to catch the evil Sinistaurs with a little help from some dino pirates. They'll find them in no time!

Quick, circle five differences in this picture.

Look out, it's T-Rex with extra Raptor back-up! Colour the battle scene.

Who's got the best super-skills, Supersaurs or Sinistaurs? Put ticks in the boxes to find out!

Supersaurs   **Sinistaurs**

	Supersaurs	Sinistaurs
Which team has the strongest dino?		
Which team has a flying dino?		
Which team has a masked dino?		
Which team has the tallest dino?		

Who has the most ticks, Supersaurs or Sinistaurs?

The winners are: ....

The Raptors are causing trouble again!
Someone call the Supersaurs...

Circle five differences in this picture.

Draw in the right Supersaur or Sinistaur to complete the sequences.

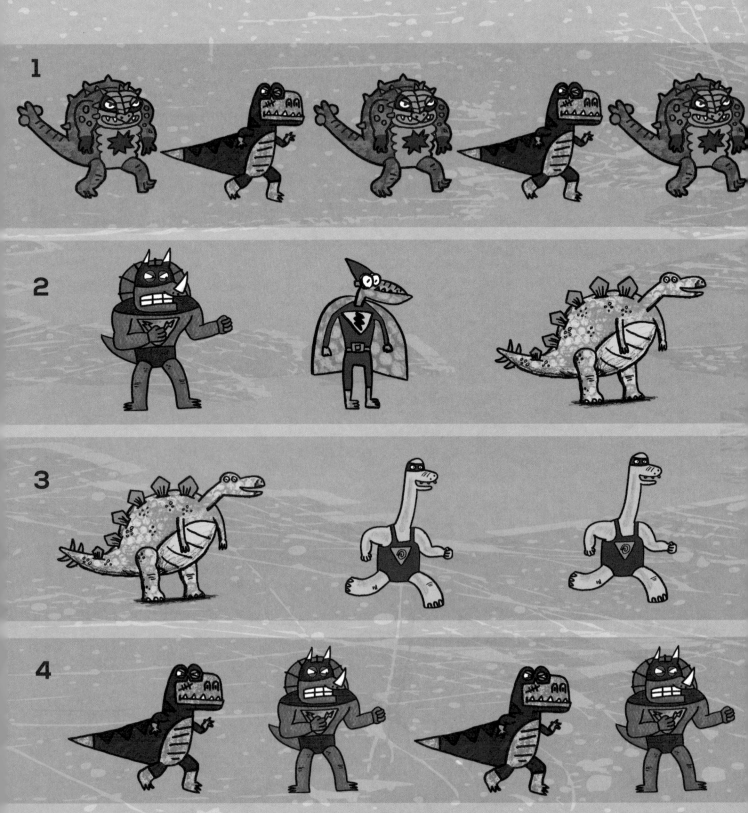

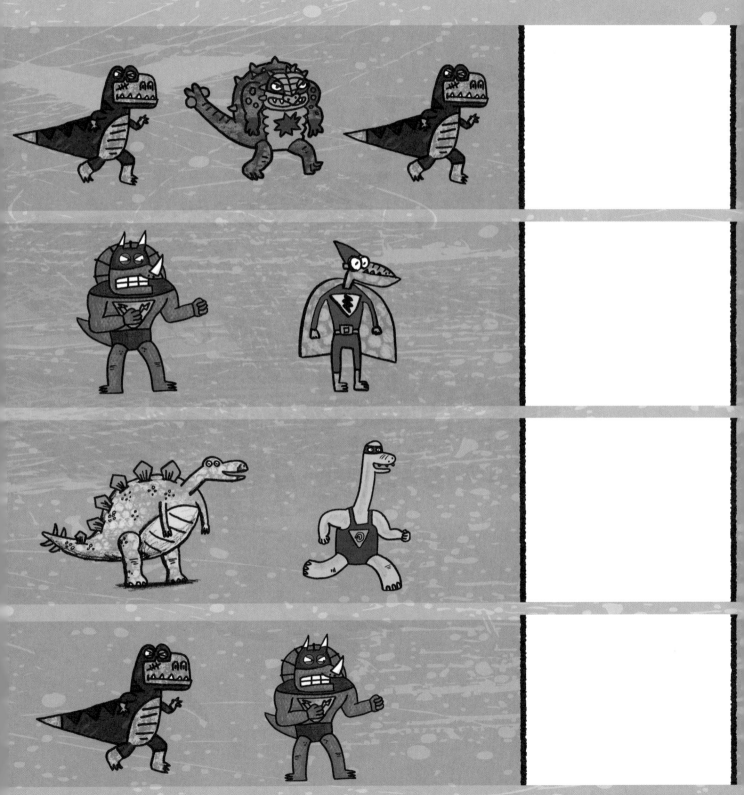

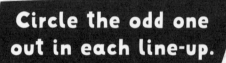
Circle the odd one out in each line-up.

1   A   B   C   D   E

2   A   B   C   D   E

3   A   B   C   D   E

4   A   B   C   D   E

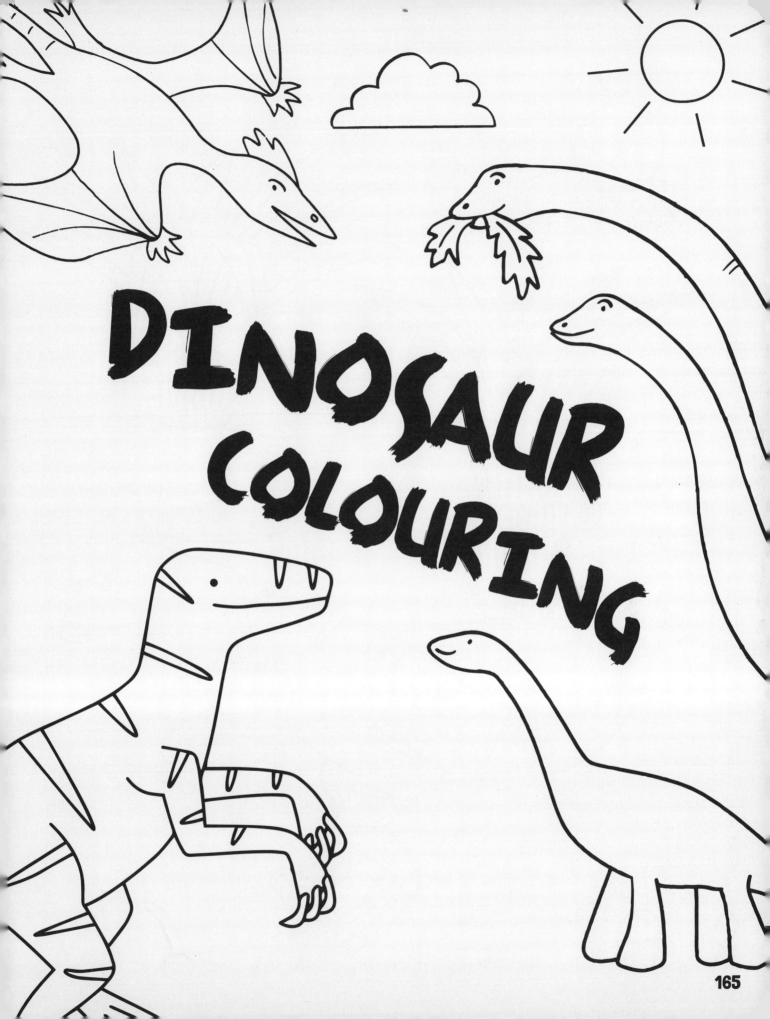

DINOSAUR COLOURING

Monster ANSWERS

Page 31

Pages 44-45

Pages 46-47
There are 9 bats.

Page 48

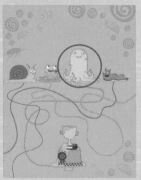

Page 50

Page 52

Page 53
Trail 3 leads to the slug monster.

Page 54

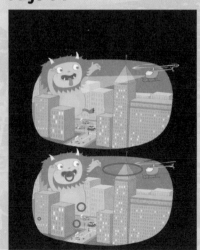

Monster ANSWERS

Page 55
The baby monsters should walk across plank 1.

Page 57
3 matches the fire monster exactly.

Page 58
There are 8 monsters.

Page 59
Smallest to tallest: 3, 2, 4, 1
Most to least number of eyes: 2, 1, 4, 3
Most to least number of feet: 3, 2, 4, 1

Pages 60-61
There are 6 little slime monsters.

Pages 62-63

Page 66
Monsters 1 and 6 look exactly the same.

Page 68
1 is eating the plate of worms.
2 is eating the cake.
3 is eating the bowl of food.

Page 69
The green monster has 8 legs.
The red monster has 10 legs.
The yellow monster has 6 legs.

P70

Page 71
There are 11 mummy monsters.

Page 72
A has the most eyes.

DINO ANSWERS

Page 123
a.2
b.4
c.1
d.3

Page 127

D	O	C	H	A	G	C	S	X
M	A	Q	R	H	R	G	U	T
P	R	L	G	N	A	B	P	Z
C	R	T	U	U	P	D	E	D
S	E	R	H	T	T	V	R	B
T	T	E	Z	R	O	Y	S	I
E	Z	X	T	I	R	V	A	T
G	K	N	A	X	S	V	U	P
O	J	O	N	R	E	N	R	V

Page 128

Pages 132-133

Page 136

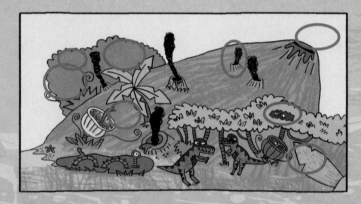

Page 146
Terra is saying:
Make room for my zoom!

Page 150
The correct route is route C.

Page 151
There are 7 spanners.

DINO ANSWERS